# The New Scribner Music Library

### DR. HOWARD HANSON

*EDITOR-IN-CHIEF*

———⟨✤⟩———

## VOLUME 10
*Art Songs*

Edited by

### PHILIP L. MILLER

———⟨✤⟩———

*CHARLES SCRIBNER'S SONS · NEW YORK*

02463

PRINTED IN THE UNITED STATES OF AMERICA
*Library of Congress Catalog Card Number 72-1497*

SBN 684-13111-0 (Volume 10)

SBN 684-13100-5 (Vols. 1-10 with Reference Volume, including Index)

# Preface

IN Volume 10 of *The New Scribner Music Library*, the distinguished musicologist and librarian Philip L. Miller turns from his delightful presentation of songs of the people in Volume 9 to another field in which he is also an acknowledged authority, the development of the Art Song.

The carefully selected songs extend from sixteenth-century composers, such as Campion, Dowland, Monteverdi, and Morley to the twentieth century's Aaron Copland and Benjamin Britten. The rich heritage of German *Lieder* is well represented not only by Schubert, Schumann, and Brahms, but also by the beautiful songs of Hugo Wolf, Carl Loewe, Robert Franz, and Richard Strauss. The Scandinavians are represented by Grieg, Sinding, and Carl Nielsen; the Russians by Glinka, Mussorgsky, Rachmaninoff, and Stravinsky. American composers include, in addition to Copland, Francis Hopkinson, Mrs. H. H. A. Beach, Charles Ives, and Edward MacDowell.

It is not too much to say that Philip Miller has compiled a volume of historical as well as musical importance.

HOWARD HANSON

# Introduction

SONG is a house of many mansions. Each of these is so vast that most listeners need a guide. This is, of course, the function of the interpreter; so we go to recitals and listen to recordings. But it is even better to have access to the printed music our favorite artists sing from. There is nothing like participation in a performance, even if it is only with our eyes and minds. Of course, no anthology can include everything, even all the best. To be representative, however, it *must* have songs in at least the standard languages—including the Russian and the Scandinavian—and it *must* take in as many as possible of the leading composers. There is also the matter of chronology—ideally there should be a sampling of every historical period.

It has been said that every man has an anthology in him. Surely every anthology should be personal—for example, I would not include in this volume any song that does not appeal to me. My task, then, is to square my personal tastes with the requirements listed above. The very vastness of the repertoire makes this possible. Beginning with the sixteenth century lutenist composers, who left us many of our most perfect songs, we must not pass over the Baroque. The great period of the German *Lied*—in which the poets became the inspiration of the composers—was followed by the similar development of the French *mélodie*. In Russia the folklike romances of Aliabiev and Varlamov gave place to the remarkable songs of Glinka, Dargomyzhsky, and Mussorgsky. The Scandinavians had their Grieg, to be followed by such men as Sibelius and Nielsen. If Purcell remains the chief glory of British music of the past, some great songs have come out of contemporary England. And we in America are coming to realize that we too have a heritage of which we may be proud.

It has been my aim in this volume to document as far as possible the history of song as I have so briefly outlined it above. Within the limitations of space I trust I have come out fairly well. But there are certain barriers that make complete success impossible. Because of copyright restrictions I have had to slight a number of contemporaries who should certainly be included. Men like Poulenc, Hindemith, Barber—even Griffes—are regretfully missing. Still, it is my hope that this anthology may prove a useful guide as well as a source of enjoyment.

PHILIP L. MILLER

# Contents by Composers

# List of Titles

*to the Browning Society of Boston*

# The Year's at the Spring

Robert Browning (1812-1889)
*(from "Pippa passes")*

Op. 44 No. 1

Mrs. H.H.A. Beach
(1867 - 1944)

**Allegro di molto**

right, _____ All's right with the

world! _____

S.M.L.10

# Zärtliche Liebe

*Tender Love*

(first published 1803)

Karl Friedrich Herrosee (1754-1821)
*English version by Robert Hess*

Ludwig van Beethoven
(1770 - 1827)

**Andante**

Ich lie - be dich, so wie du mich, am A - bend und am
*I love you, dear, as you love me, At eve - ning and at*

Mor - gen, noch war kein Tag, wo du und ich nicht
*morn - ing. No_ day has passed that you and I Our*

teil - ten uns - re_ Sor - gen.
*cares could not be_ scorn - ing.*

Auch
*Our_*

# Die Nachtigall

*The Nightingale*

Theodor Storm (1817-1888)
*English version by Robert Hess*

Alban Berg
(1885-1935)

# Absence

Op. 7 No. 4

from *Les Nuits d'Été* (1834)

Théophile Gautier (1811-1872)
*English version by Robert Hess*

Hector Berlioz
(1803-1869)

Re-viens, re-viens,_ ma bien ai-mé - - e!
*Re-turn, re-turn,_ my love, I'm cry - ing,*

Comme u - ne fleur loin du so-leil,_ La fleur_ de ma vie_ est fer-
*As would a flower far from the light; The flower of my life_ now is*

mé - e,_ Loin de ton sou-ri - re ver-meil.
*dy - ing,_ Far from your sweet smile so warm and bright.*

S.M.L. 10

Un poco animato

En - tre nos cœurs qu'el - le dis - tan - ce, Tant d'es - pace en - tre nos bai-
*Be-tween our hearts how vast a dis-tance; Now my long-ing can-not be*

*pp*

con agitazione

sers! O sort a - mer, o dure ab - sen - ce,
*stilled. O bit - ter fate with cruel in - sis - tance,*

*mf*

Tempo I

*f*

O grands dé - sirs in - ap - pai - sés!
*O great de-sire so un - ful-filled!*

*f*

*p*

20

Re-viens, re-viens,__ ma bien ai - mé - e!
Re-turn, re-turn,__ my love, I'm cry - ing,

Comme u - ne fleur__ loin du so - leil,__ La fleur__ de ma vie - est fer-
As would a flower far from the light; The flower of my life__ now is

mé - e,__ Loin de ton sou - ri - re ver-meil.
dy - ing,__ Far from your sweet smile so warm and bright.

S.M.L. 10

*sotto voce ed estinto*

Re-viens, re - viens,_ ma bien ai - mé - e! Comme u - ne
*Re-turn, re - turn,_ my love, I'm cry - ing, As would a*

fleur_ loin du so - leil,_ La fleur_ de ma vie est fer-
*flower_ far from the light;_ The flower of my life_ now is*

mé - e,_ Loin de ton sou - ri - re ver-meil!
*dy - ing,_ Far from your sweet smile so warm and bright.*

# In stiller Nacht

*In Night so Still*

from *49 Deutsche Volkslieder* (pub. 1894)

Traditional
*English version by Robert Hess*

Johannes Brahms
(1833-1897)

her - bem Leid und Trau - rig-keit ist mir das Herz zer-
*mourn - ful song heard all night long, Its grief my heart is*

flos - sen, die Blü - me-lein, mit Trä - nen rein hab
*rend - ing, The flow - ers dear, my ev - 'ry tear Has*

ich sie all be - gos - sen.
*wat - ered with - out end - ing.*

Vo - gel-sang noch Freu - den-klang man hö - ret in den
*song of bird can now be heard, To nest they're all re-*

Lüf - ten, die wil - den Tier' trau'rn auch mit mir in
*pair - ing. The beasts so wild with moan - ing mild Will*

Stei - nen und in Klüf - ten.
*join me in de - spair - ing.*

# Wiegenlied

*Cradle Song*

Op. 49 No. 4

Words from "Des Knaben Wunderhorn"
*English version by Arthur Westbrook*

Johannes Brahms

**Con moto** *(dolce)*

1. Gu-ten A - bend, gut' Nacht, mit Ro - sen be - dacht,_ mit_ Näg-lein be - steckt, schlüpf' un - ter die Deck': Mor-gen früh, wenn Gott will, wirst du wie - der ge - weckt, mor-gen früh, wenn Gott will, wirst du wie - der ge - weckt.

1. Lull-a - by and good - night! With ros - es be - dight;_ Creep in - to thy_ bed, There pil - low thy head. If God will, thou shalt wake When the morn - ing doth break, If God will, thou shalt wake When the morn - ing doth break.

# Wie Melodien zieht es mir

*A Thought like Haunting Music*

Op. 105 No. 1

Klaus Groth (1819-1899)
*English version by Robert Hess*

Johannes Brahms

Zart (*Delicately*)

Wie Me - lo - di - en   zieht   es   mir
*A thought like haunt - ing  mu - sic runs*

*p sempre dolce*

lei - se durch   den Sinn,   wie Früh - lings-blu - men
*gent - ly through   my mind,   Like flowers that bloom in*

blüht   es, und   schwebt wie Duft   da - hin,
*spring - time, its   fra - grance wafts be - hind,*

und schwebt wie Duft da - hin.
*its fra - grance wafts be - hind.*

Doch kommt das Wort und fasst es und führt es vor das
*But should a word a - rise to de - fine be-fore my*

Aug', wie Ne - bel-grau er-blasst es und schwin-det wie ein
*eye, Like mist the thought would van - ish and dwin - dle like a*

dim.

Hauch,
sigh,

und schwin-det wie ein Hauch.
and dwin-dle like a sigh.

Und den-noch ruht_ im_
And yet a hid - den_

Rei - me ver-bor-gen wohl ein Duft,
fra-grance re - mains with-in the rhyme,

den mild aus stil - lem
And gent - ly from its

*For my Mother*

# The Birds
### (1929/1934)

Hilaire Belloc
(1870-1953)

Benjamin Britten
(*b.* 1913)

When Je - sus Christ was four years old, The an - gels brought Him toys of gold, Which no man ev - er had bought or sold.

S M.L. 10

**Poco animando**

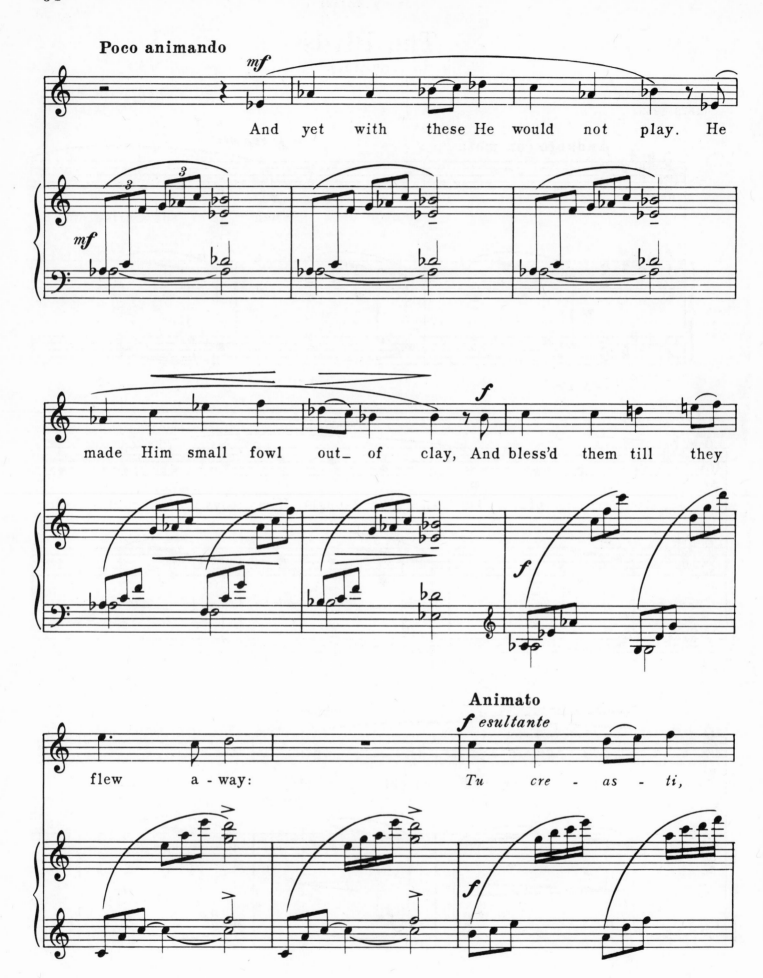

And yet with these He would not play. He
made Him small fowl out of clay, And bless'd them till they
flew a - way:

**Animato**

*Tu cre - as - ti,*

Molto tranquillo

*morendo*

*pp solenne*

Do - mi - ne.

Je - sus Christ, Thou

*morendo*

*(lunga)*

*mf*

*p*

*pp solenne*

child so wise, Bless mine hands and fill mine eyes,

And

*ppp*

*una corda*

*Ped.*

**Molto più lento**

*rall.*

bring my soul to Par - a - dise.

*rall.*

*ppp*

*più p*

*tre corde*

*una corda*

# The Cypress Curtain of the Night
### (1601)

Thomas Campion

Thomas Campion
(1567 - 1620)
*Edited by Edmund H. Fellowes*

The cy - press cur - tain of the night is
Yet oft my trem - bling eyes through faint - ness
Grief, seize my soul, for that will still en -

spread, And o - ver all a si - lent dew is
close; And then the map of hell be - fore me
dure When my crazed bod - y is con - sumed and

cast. The weak - er cares by sleep are con - quer -
stands, Which ghosts do see, and I am one of
gone; Bear it to thy black den, there keep it

*To Arthur Berger*

# The Chariot

from *Twelve Poems of Emily Dickinson* (1948-50)

Emily Dickinson
(1830 - 1886)

Aaron Copland
(*b.* 1900)

Be-cause I would not stop for Death, ____

He kind-ly stopped for me; ____ The car-riage

More slowly (♩ = 66)

held but just our-selves___ and Im-mor-tal-i - ty._____ We

slow-ly drove,____ He knew no haste, And I had put a-way___

___ My la - bor,___ and my leis-ure too, For his ci-vil-i - ty.___

**As at first** (♩ = 76)

We passed the school where chil-dren

*a trifle faster* (♩ = 88)

played, Their les-sons scarce-ly done; We passed the fields of

gaz - ing grain, _____ We passed _____ the

*a trifle broader* (♩ = 69)

Since then 'tis cen-tu-ries; but each Feels

short-er than the day I first sur - mised The hors-es' heads Were

(♩ = 72) *poco rit.*

toward e-ter-ni - ty.

# Beau Soir

*Evening Fair*

Paul Bourget (1852-1935)
*English version by Robert Hess*

Claude Debussy
(1862-1918)

**Andante, ma non troppo**

Lorsque      au so-leil cou-chant      les ri -
*When      in the sun-set glow      all the*

viè - res      sont      ro - ses,      Et qu'un tiè - de fris -
*riv - ers      are      glid - ing,      And through fields warm and*

44

son court sur les champs de blé,————
gold the cares of day de - part,————

Un con - seil d'être heu - reux sem - ble sor - tir des cho - ses
From this scene a sug - ges - tion to be glad con - fid - ing,

Et mon - ter vers le cœur— trou - blé.
Seems to rise in the troub - led heart.

# Come Again!

from *First Booke of Ayres* (1597)

Anon. (1597)
(possibly by Dowland)
*Keyboard adaptation of the lute accompaniment*
*by Kurt Stone*

John Dowland
(1562-1626)

[Andante]

*mp espressivo*

*mp*

1. Come a-gain! Sweet love doth now in-vite Thy grac - es,
2. Come a-gain! That I may cease to mourn Through thy un -
3. Gen-tle Love, Draw forth thy wound - ing dart, Thou canst not

that re-frain To do me due de-light, To see, to hear, to touch, to kiss,
kind dis-dain. For now, left and for-lorn, I sit, I sigh, I weep, I faint,
pierce her heart; For I, that to ap-prove, By sighs and tears more hot than are

*p cresc. poco a poco*

*p cresc. poco a poco*

*f*

to die — With thee a - gain in sweet-est sym - pa - thy.
I die — In dead - ly pain and end-less mis - e - ry.
thy shafts, Did tempt, while she, while she for tri - umph laughs.

*dim.*

*mp*

*mf*

*dim.*

*p*

S.M.L. 10

# Automne

*Fall*

Op. 18 No. 3

d'Armand Silvestre
*English version by Bernard Taylor*

Gabriel Fauré
(1845 - 1924)

Andante moderato (♩. = 66)

very legato but with strong left hand accent

sempre legato

Au - tom - ne au ciel bru-meux, aux
The dy - ing days of Fall, so

ho - ri - zons na vrants, ___
dim, so grey and cold, ___

es,
drops,

Et mon-ter   á   mes yeux,   des
And   my   eyes   fill   with tears,   the

lar-mes,qu'en mon cœur   Mes vingt ans_____ a-vaient   ou-bli-
tears that fill   my heart   For   the   years_____   my youth   has   for-

é   -   -   es!
got   -   -   ten!

# Aus meinen grossen Schmerzen

*Deep from My Soul's Dejection*

Op. 5 No. 1

Heinrich Heine (1799-1856)
*English version by Robert Hess*

Robert Franz
(1815 - 1892)

Andante (Innig/Fervently)

Aus mei-nen gro-ssen Schmer-zen mach ich die klei-nen
*Deep from my soul's de - jec - tion These lit - tle songs I*

Lie - der, die he - ben ihr klin - gend Ge - fie - der und
*fash - ion, Which fly on their swift wings of pas - sion To*

flat - tern nach ih - rem Her - zen. Sie
*seek my true love's af - fec - tion. They*

fan - den den Weg zur Trau - ten, doch kom - men sie wie - der und
*found her, my thoughts re - lay - ing, And now have re-turned to me*

kla - gen, und kla - gen, und wol - len nicht sa - gen, was
*weep - ing, Though weep-ing, their se - cret they're keep - ing, Of*

sie im Her - zen schau - ten.
*what her heart was say - ing.*

# The Lark

## Жаворонокъ

Nestor Kukolnik (1809-1868)
*English version by Robert Hess*

Mikhail Glinka
(1804-1857)

Moderato

*p sempre e molto con anima*

Меж - ду не - бомъ
*High a - bove the*

и зем-лей Пѣ - сня раз - да-ет - ся, Не-ис-ход-но-
*earth so_fair, one can hear her sing - ing Float-ing on the*

S.M.L. 10

И вздохнетъ у - крад - кой, Кто - то вспомнитъ про ме - ня,
*You, who know my sad - ness, Let my thoughts your love in-spire,*

И вздохнетъ у - крад - кой.
*You, who know my sad - ness.*

# Jeg Elsker Dig!

*I Love You!*

Op. 5 No. 3

Hans Christian Andersen (1805-1875)
*English version by Philip L. Miller*

Edvard Grieg
(1843-1907)

Min Tan-kes
*My deep-est*

Tan-ke e - ne Du er vor-den,
*thoughts, my all to you I'm giv-ing,*

Du er mit
*You my first*

Hjer-tes før - ste Kaer-lig-hed,
*dream, my on - ly love shall be;*

jeg el-sker
*I love you*

*á Léon Daudet*

# D'une Prison

*From a Prison*

(1892)

"Par dessus le mur de ma fenêtre... je voyais, c'était en Août, se balancer la cime aux feuilles voluptueusement frémissantes de quelque haut peuplier d'un square ou d'un boulevard voisin. En même temps m'arrivaient des rumeurs lointaines, adoucies, de fête..."

Paul Verlaine (MES PRISONS)

"Over the wall outside my window... I saw—it was in August—the waving top and the luxuriant, quivering leaves of a tall poplar in a park or by a neighboring street. At the same time, sounds of merrymaking came to me, mellowed by distance..."

Paul Verlaine (MY PRISONS)

Paul Verlaine (1844-1896)
*English version by Robert Hess*

Reynaldo Hahn
(1875-1947)

Pas trop lent *(Not too slow)*

Le / The

*Les deux pédales constamment (Both pedals throughout)*

*avec la plus grande tranquillité (with the greatest tranquility)*

ciel est, par des-sus le toit, si bleu, si cal - me... Un
*blue sky seen a-cross the roof, no cloud dis-play - ing... A*

63

S.M.L.10

Dieu, mon Dieu! La vie est là simple et tran - quil - le!...
*God, my God! The sim-ple life out-side is flow - ing;...*

cresc. espress.

Cet - te pai - si - ble ru-meur là vient de la vil - le...
*The peace-ful sounds at first a - rise... now they are go - ing.*

**Un peu plus lent, et douloureux**
*(A little slower, and sadly)*

Qu'as-tu fait, ô toi que voi - là pleu-rant sans ces - se,
*Tell me this, o you, who are weep-ing with-out meas - ure,*

molto espr.

Dis!— qu'as-tu fait,— toi que voi - là, de ta jeu - nes - se?
*Say!— Tell me this:— what have you done with youth's first treas - ure?*

Le ciel est, par des-sus le toit, si bleu, si cal -
*The blue sky seen a-cross the roof, no cloud dis-play -*

- me!...
*- ing...*

# She Never Told Her Love

William Shakespeare
(1564 - 1616)

Joseph Haydn
(1732 - 1809)

**Largo assai, e con espressione**

She nev - er told her love, She

nev-er told her love, But let con-ceal-ment, like a worm in the

bud, Feed on her dam - ask cheek;

She

sat     like pa-tience    on a mon-u-ment, Smil - ing,   smil - ing at__

_p dolce_

grief,                                                  Smil-ing, smil - ing at

[sim.]

grief.

fp          fp          pp

# The Spirit's Song

Anna Hunter (1742?-1821?)

Joseph Haydn

sor - row o'er the tomb,_ Nor_ sor-row o'er the tomb,

My spir - it wan-ders free, My spir - it wan-ders free, And

waits, and_ waits till_ thine shall come.

All

pen - sive and a - lone,___ I see thee sit and weep,___ Thy

head up-on the stone, Where my cold ash - es___ sleep, Where___

_____ my cold ash - es___ sleep.

I watch thy speak-ing eyes,___ And mark each fall-ing

72

S.L.M. 10

# My Days Have Been so Wondrous Free

(1759 ?)

Francis Hopkinson

Melody and Bass by
**Francis Hopkinson**
(1737-1791)
*Keyboard realization by Kurt Stone*

My days have been so_ won-drous free, The lit-tle_ birds_ that_

fly With care-less ease from tree_ to tree Were but as_ blest as_

I, Were but_ as blest as I.

Ask gliding waters if a tear Of mine increased their stream. And ask the breathing gales if e'er I lent a sigh to them, I lent a sigh to them.

*à B. et C.*

# Berceuse

Authors (both texts) unknown

Mary Howe
(1882 - 1964)

Sleep well, you lit-tle young one,
*Dors, dors, le pe-tit gos - se,*

'Tis the end of day. One ti - ny lit-tle star - let
*C'est la fin du jour. Une seule pe-tite é - toi - le*

Takes his turn at play. See, ev'n the pret-ty flow'rs
*S'é-veille à son tour. Vois même les jo-lies fleurs*

Copyright 1925, 1944 by the Estate of Mary Howe; reprinted by permission.

Will dream as turn the hours. Sleep then, you
*Vont rê - ver tout á l'heure.* *Dors, dors, le*

*poco rit.*

lit-tle young one, 'Tis the end of day.
*pe-tit gos - se, C'est la fin du jour.*

*a tempo*

*rit.*

*a tempo*

78

Sleep well, you lit-tle young one, Night is all a - round.
*Dors, dors, le pe-tit gos - se, Il fait dé - jà nuit.*

Time ev - 'ry-thing was rest - ing, Not the small - est sound.
*C'est l'heure où tout re-po - se, Pas le moin - dre bruit,*

All lit - tle hearts be still, Noth - ing shall work you ill.
*Tran quils les pe-tits cœurs, Rien ne leur fe - ra peur.*

Sleep then, you lit-tle young one, Night is all a-
*Dors, dors, le pe-tit gos - se, Il fait dé - jà*

round, All lit-tle birds are safe-ly
*nuit. Tous les pe - tits__ oi-seaux sont*

in their nest. (Lit - tle Je - sus, watch o - ver him.)
*dans leurs nids. Pe-tit Jé - su, veil - lez sur lui.*

# Charlie Rutlage

(1921?)

Traditional *

Charles E. Ives
(1874 - 1954)

In moderate time

An - oth-er good cow-punch-er has gone to meet his fate, I hope_ _he'll find__ a rest - ing__ place, with - in the gold-en gate, the gold - en gate. An - oth - er place is va-cant on the ranch of the X I T, 'Twill be

* from Cowboy Songs and other Frontier Ballads; collected by John A. Lomax, M.A. (University of Texas), The Macmillan Co., New York.

** All bracketed indications are editorial additions.

hard to find an-oth-er that's liked as well as he. The first that died was—

— Kid White, a man both tough and brave,— While Char-lie

Rut-lage makes the third— to be sent— to his grave, Caused———

*as he rode the round up,*    *a*    XIT *turned back to the herd;*    Poor

*Char-lie shoved him in a-gain, his*    *cut-ting horse he spurred;*    An -

*oth-er turned; at that mo-ment*    *his horse the crea-ture spied*    *and turned and*

\* In these measures the notes are indicated only approximately; the time, of course, is the main point.

86

S.M.L.10

# Walking

### (1902)

Charles E. Ives

Charles E. Ives

**Allegro con spirito**

A big Oc-to-ber morn-ing, the vil-lage church-bells, the

road a-long the ridge,— the chest-nut burr and su-mach, the hills a-bove the

88

bridge—with au-tumn col-ors glow.

Now we strike a stead-y gait, walk-ing towards the fu-ture,

let-ting past and pres-ent wait, we push on in the sun. Now hark! Some-

S.M.L. 10

But we keep on a-walk-ing, 'tis yet not noon-day, the road still calls us on-ward, to-day we do not choose to die or to dance, but to live and walk.

*più decresc. non rall.*

# Es muss ein Wunderbares sein

## It Must Be Wonderful Indeed

Oskar von Redwitz (1823-1891)
*English version by Robert Hess*

Franz Liszt
(1811-1886)

*Schwebend (Floating)*

Es muss ein Wun - der - ba - res sein ums
*It must be won - der - ful in - deed for*

Lie - ben zwei - er See - len,
*love to be re - veal - ing,*
sich schlie - ssen ganz ein - an - der ein, sich
*Two souls ful - fill - ing ev - 'ry need, with*

nie ein Wort ver - heh - len,
*not a word con - ceal - ing;*
und Freud' und Leid __
*In joy and grief, __*
und Glück und Not __
*with ev - 'ry breath __*

# Edward

Op.1 No.1

Johann Gottfried von Herder (1744-1803)
*English version adapted from an old Scottish ballad*

Carl Loewe
(1796-1869)

drückt ein an-drer Schmerz.    O!"    "Ich hab ge-schla-gen mei-nen
*oth - er dule ye dree,\**    *O!"*    *"O I hae strick-en my*

Va - ter tot!    Mut - ter!    Mut - ter! Ich hab ge-schla-gen mei-nen
*fa - ther dead,*    *Moth - er,*    *Moth - er; O I hae strick - en my*

Va - ter tot, und das,    das quält mein Herz!    O!"___
*fa - ther dead, A - las,*    *ah, wae is me,*    *O!"___*

will wan-dern ü - bers Meer!
*And I'll fare o'er the sea,*

O!"
*O!"*

"Und was soll wer-den dein Hof und
*"What will ye do wi' your house and*

Hall? Ed-ward, Ed-ward!
*ha', Ed-ward, Ed-ward?*

Und was soll wer-den dein Hof und
*What will ye do wi' your house and*

Hall? so herr-lich sonst, so schön. O!"
*ha' That were sae fair to see, O?"*

100

"Und was soll wer-den aus Weib und Kind? Ed-ward, Ed-ward!
"What will ye leave to your bairns and wife, Ed-ward, Ed-ward?

Und was soll wer-den aus Weib und Kind, wann du gehst ü-bers
What will ye leave to your bairns and wife, When ye gang o'er the

Meer? O!" "Die Welt ist
sea, O?" "The warld is

gross, lass sie_ bet-teln drin, Mut-ter, Mut-ter! Die Welt ist gross,_
wide, let_ them beg through life, Moth-er, Moth-er; The warld is wide,_

# Süsses Begräbnis

*Sweet Burial*

Op. 62 No. 4

Friedrich Rückert (1788-1866)
*English version by Robert Hess*

Carl Loewe

dich so süss _____ be - gra - ben!
*grave so sweet - ly cov' - ered!*

Al - le Lüf - te ha-ben ge - stöh - net,
*All the breez - es sad -ly are sing - ing,*

Mai - en-glok-ken zu Grab dir ge - tö - net,
*Blue - bells dirg - es so soft -ly are ring - ing,*

# Long Ago

Op. 56 No. 1

Edward MacDowell

Edward MacDowell
(1861 - 1908)

Long a - go, _____ sweet - heart mine, Ros - es bloomed as ne'er be - fore, Long a - go _____ the world was young For us, \_\_ sweet-heart. Fields of vel - vet, a - zure skies, \_\_ Whis-p'ring

*pp very softly*

# The Sea

Op. 47 No.7

William Dean Howells (1837-1920)

Edward MacDowell

111

S.M.L.10

# Ich bin der Welt abhanden gekommen
*Lost to the World*

Friedrich Rückert (1788-1866)
*English version by Robert Hess and Philip L. Miller*

Gustav Mahler
(1860-1911)

Ich bin der Welt_____ ab - han - den ge - kom - men,
*Un - to the world_____ I am lost\_ for - ev - er,*

# Élégie

Louis Gallet (1835-1898)
*English version by Charlotte H. Coursen*

Jules Massenet
(1842-1912)

119

S. M. L. 10

120

S.M.L. 10

# Die Liebende schreibt
## *Love Letter*
### Op. 86 No.3

Johann Wolfgang von Goethe (1749-1832)
*English version by Robert Hess and Philip L. Miller*

Felix Mendelssohn
(1809-1847)

Ein Blick von dei-nen Au-gen in die mei - nen, ein
*One glance from your dear eyes to mine I treas - ure,* *One*

Kuss von deinem Mund auf mei-nem Mun - de, wer da-von hat, wie ich, ge-wis-se
*kiss from your dear lips to mine in greet - ing, Who-ev-er knows, as I, of such a*

Kun-de, mag dem was anders wohl er-freu-lich_ schei - nen? Ent-fernt von dir, ent-
*meet-ing, Noth-ing on earth can give one so_ much_ pleas - ure. A-way from you, e-*

frem-det von den Meinen, führ ich nur die Ge - dan-ken in die Run-de, und im-mer treffen
*stranged from those a-round me, Haunt - ed ev - er by thoughts that keep re-peat - ing, And ev - er call-ing*

sie auf je - ne Stun-de, die ein - - - zi-ge; da fang ich
*back to mind that meet - ing, Our on - - - ly one, I think with*

an zu wei - - - - - - - - nen.
*bit - ter weep - - - - - - - ing.*

Die Trä - ne trock - net wie
*Then all___ at once I end___*

- der un-ver-se - hens: er liebt ja, denk ich, her in die-se Stil - le,
*my fool-ish cry - ing; "I love you!" I im - ag-ine you are say - ing,*

und soll-test du nicht in die Fer - ne rei - chen?
*And hope that you will hear my thought as spo - ken.*

Ver - nimm das Lis - peln
*Re - ceive this whis - pered*

die - ses Lie - be-we - hens; mein ein-zig Glück auf Er - den ist dein Wil - le, dein
*pledge of love un-dy - ing! My on-ly joy, your will to be o - bey - ing, Your*

# Der Mond
*The Moon*
Op. 86 No. 5

Emanuel Geibel (1815-1884)
*English version by Robert Hess and Philip L. Miller*

Felix Mendelssohn

Mein Herz ist wie die dunk-le Nacht, wenn al - le Wi - pfel rau - schen; da steigt der Mond in vol - ler Pracht aus Wol - ken sacht — und

*My heart is like the dark-est night, When whis-p'ring trees are bend - ing; The moon comes out in splen - dor bright, From cloud - ed height, And*

# Durandarte

## (Romanza)

### (1536)

Anon.
*English version by Robert Hess*

Luis Milán*
(c.1500 - c.1561)

**Moderato** *(do not drag)*

1. Du - ran - dar - te, Du - ran - dar - te,
2. Cuan - doen ga - las yin - ven - cio - nes
1. *Du - ran - dar - te, Du - ran - dar - te,*
2. *You had sworn to love on - ly me,*

Buen ca - ba - lle - ro
Pu - bli - ca - bas tu
*Good cav - a - lier of*
*When at those cel - e -*

pro - ba - do.
cuy - da - do.
*bright - est fame.*
*bra - tions gay.*

* Keyboard adaptation by Kurt Stone of the lute *(vihuela)* accompaniment.

A - cor -- dár - se -- te de - bri -- a
A - go -- ra des - co - no - ci -- do,
*Can you* *not re -* *call those brave* *days,*
*You could* *not be* *faith-ful to* *me —*

D'a -- quel buen tiem - po pa -- sa -
Di, por -- que me has ol -- vi - da -
*Those* *fine* *days* *when all knew_ your_ great*
*How* *soon* *you* *did for - get_ that_ first*

do.
do?
*name?*
*day!*

130

S.M.L.10

131

S.M.L.10

# Maledetto sia l'aspetto

*Lover Hateful*

Author unknown

*English version by Robert Hess*

Claudio Monteverdi
(1567 - 1643)
*Continuo realization by Kurt Stone*

**Allegretto**

1. Ma - le - det - to  sia l'as - pet - to  che m'ar - de tri - sto me  poi ch'io
1. Lov - er_ hate - ful,  So _ un - grate - ful,  On - ly_ bring - ing me  pain!  First you

sen - to  rio tor - men - to  poi ch'io mo - ro  ne ri - sto - ro ha mia fè sol per
hurt me  And de - sert me,  Then for - get me  While you let me go on liv - ing in

te  Ma - le - det - to  sia l'as - pet - to  che_ m'ar - de tri - sto  me.
vain.  Lov - er_ hate - ful,  So_ un - grate - ful,  On - ly_ bring - ing me  pain.

# It Was a Lover and His Lass

(First published in 1600)

*Text used (written?) by*
William Shakespeare (1564-1616)
*in* "As You Like It"

Thomas Morley*
(1557 - 1603)

1. It was a lov-er and his lass,
2. Be-tween the a-cres of the rye,
3. Then pret-ty lov-ers take their time,

With a hey, with a ho, and a hey non-ie no, and a hey_____ non-ie non-ie no,

That o'er the green corn-fields did pass
These pret-ty coun-try fools would lie
For love is crown-ed with the prime

in Spring-time, in

* Keyboard realization by Kurt Stone of the original lute tablature.

136

S.M.L. 10

# Abendempfindung

*Evening Mood*

K.523

Joachim Heinrich Campe (1746-1818)
*English version by Robert Hess*
*and Philip L. Miller*

Wolfgang Amadeus Mozart
(1756-1791)

A - bend ist's, die
*Eve - ning falls,* *the*

Son - ne ist ver - schwun - den und der
*sun has set in splen - - dor;* *And the*

Mond strahlt Sil - ber - glanz;
*sil - ver moon will — rise.*

so ent-flieh'n des_ Le-bens schön-ste_ Stun-den, flieh'n vor - ü - ber wie im
*Now the fleet - ing_ hours of_ life so_ ten - der Dance a - way be - fore my*

Tanz.
*eyes.*

Bald ent-flieht des_ Le-bens bun - te_
*Soon the stage of_ life will_ fade in_*

Sce-ne, und der Vor-hang rollt her - ab;
*shad-ow, And the cur-tain will de-scend.*

aus ist un - ser Spiel,
*Now our play is done!*

des Freun-des Trä - ne__
*and on our grave__ Are__*

Ruh'. / fair.

Werd't ihr_ dann an_ / If_ you_ come be-

mei-nem Gra - be wei - nen, trau - ernd mei - ne / side my grave with weep - ing, Shed - ding all_____ your

A - sche sehn, dann, o Freun-de, will ich euch er-schei-nen und will / bit - ter tears, Then look up to heav-en for my greet-ing As a

him - mel - auf euch weh'n. / shin - ing_ star ap - pears.

Schenk' auch du ein Trän - chen mir, und pflü - cke mir ein
*On - ly shed for me one tear, And gath - er one small*

Veil-chen auf mein Grab, und mit dei - nem see - len-
*vio-let from my grave; With your soul - ful glanc - es*

vol - len Bli-cke sieh' dann sanft auf mich her-ab, sieh' dann
*bid fare - well: Let them show the love you gave, Let them*

sanft, sieh' dann sanft auf mich her - ab.
*show, let them show the love you gave.*

Weih' mir ei - ne Trä - ne, und
*Shed for me one tear - drop, and*

ach! schä-me dich nur nicht, sie mir zu weih'n o sie wird in_ mei -
*ah, Do not be a - shamed, it_ falls for me;___ In my di - a - dem___*

- nem Di - a - de - me dann die schön - ste_ Per - le
*___ that tear shall_ glis-ten, And a love - ly___ pearl shall*

sein,_ o_ sie_ wird_ in_ mei - nem Di - a - de - me
*be,_ In_ my_ di - a - dem___ that tear shall_ glis - ten,*

# Das Veilchen

*The Violet*

K. 476

Wolfgang von Goethe (1749-1832)
*English version by Robert Hess*

Wolfgang Amadeus Mozart

Ein Veil-chen auf der Wie - se stand, ge-
*A vio - let in the mead - ow grew, De-*

bückt in sich und un - be-kannt: es war ein her- zig's Veil - chen. Da
*mure and shy it hid from view, It was a charm-ing vio - let. One*

kam ein' jun-ge Schä-fe-rin mit leich-tem Schritt und mun - term Sinn da-
*day a love-ly shep-herd lass Came light - ly trip - ping through the grass This*

her, da - her, die Wie - se— her und— sang.
*way, this way a - cross the— field, and— sang.*

nur, ach_ nur ein Vier-tel-stünd-chen lang.
*haps, per - haps for just a lit - tle while.*

Ach, a - ber ach! das Mäd-chen kam und nicht in
*Ah, but a - las! the maid-en came, And to the*

Acht das Veil-chen nahm, er-trat____ das ar - me Veil-chen. Es
*flow-er's deep-est shame She tram - pled that poor vio - let. It*

# Triste estaba el rey David

*David the King Was Sorrowful*

(Romanza)

Alonso Mudarra
(c.1508-1580)
*Edited by Kurt Stone*

*English version by Robert Hess*

\* The accompaniment was intended for the *vihuela*, the early Spanish lute. It may be played on a lute or a guitar.

# After the Battle
## Забытый

Arsenyi Golenishchev-Kutuzov
(1848 - 1913)
*English version by*
*Geo. Harris, Jr., and Kurt Schindler*

A Ballad
(1874)

Modeste Mussorgsky
(1839 - 1881)

**Alla marcia** *(sostenuto, ma non troppo)*

Он смерть на-шёл в кра-ю чу-жом, в кра-
*He met his death in for-eign land, In*

ю чу-жом, в бо-ю, с вра-гом, но враг дру-зья-ми по-беж-дён, дру-
*bit-ter fight-ing, hand to hand; His friends have won the vic-to-ry. And*

зья ли-ку-ют, толь-ко он, на по-ле бит-вы по-за-быт, о-дин ле-жит. И
*they are shout-ing. On-ly he, For-got-ten un-der-neath the skies, A-lone he lies. And*

меж - ду тем как жад-ный вран пьёт кровь е - го из све-жих ран и
*down there sweeps a greed-y crow To drink his blood that still doth flow, He*

то - чит, не за-кры-тый глаз, гро-зив-ший смер-тью в смер - ти час, и,
*picks his eyes that still do glow'r With death-ly glance in death's own hour; He*

на - сла - див-шись, пьян и сыт, до - лой ле-тит... Да -
*drinks his fill, he leaves his prey And flies a - way. A -*

лё - ко там, в кра-ю род - ном,
*far at home a-cross the wild.*

con 2 Ped.

# Little Star So Bright
## Гдѣ ты, звѣздочка

(1857)

Modeste Mussorgsky
*English version by*
*Deems Taylor and Kurt Schindler*

Modeste Mussorgsky
Posthumous work, revised by V. G. Karatygin

# Genrebillede

*Period Piece*

Opus 6

Jens Peter Jakobsen (1847-1885)
*English version by Philip L. Miller and Kurt Stone*

Carl Nielsen
(1865 - 1931)

Pa - gen højt paa Taar - net sad,—
*Way up there up - on the tow'r The*

stir - red' ud saa vi - de, dig - ted' paa et El - skovs-kvad
*page sat, gaz - ing far and wide; Tried to write a hymn of love,*

om sin El-skovs-kvi - de, kun - de ik - ke faa—det sam - let,
*Think - ing of—his sweet - heart; Could not fit his thoughts to vers - es;*

158

sad og fam - led', sad og fam - led' nu med Stjer -
Sat and fum - bled, sat and grum - bled— Now the heav -

- ner, nu med Ro - ser—
- ens, now the ros - es

In - tet ri - med' sig paa Ro - ser— Ro -
(Noth-ing wants to rhyme with ros - es), Ros -

S.M.L.10

# Evening Hymn

*On a Ground*

William Fuller
Lord Bishop of Lincoln
(1608-1675)

Henry Purcell
(c.1659-1695)
Arranged by W.G.Whittaker

soft_____ Bed, to the soft,_ the soft_ Bed _ my Bod-y I__ dis-pose, but where, where shall my soul_ re-pose? Dear,____ dear ____ God, _ e-ven in Thy Arms, ev'n_ — in_ Thy_ Arms, and can there be an - y so

sweet _____ se - cu - ri - ty! Can there

be, an - y so sweet, so sweet se - cu - ri-

ty! Then to thy rest, _____ O __ my

Soul! Then to thy rest, _____ O __ my_

54

164

Hal - le - lu - jah, Hal - le - lu - - - jah, Hal -

- - - - le - lu - jah, Hal - - - -

- - - - le - lu - jah, Hal - le - lu - jah, Hal - le-

lu - - - jah, Hal - - - - le - lu -

# Music for a While

From *Oedipus* by
John Dryden (1631-1700) and Nathan Lee (1657-1693)

Henry Purcell
*Continuo realization by Kurt Stone*

eas'd, ___ eas'd, ___ eas'd, ___ And dis -

dain - ing_ to be_pleas'd, Till A - lec - to free _____ the_

dead, till A - lec - - to_ free_ the_dead From

their e - ter - - - - nal, e - ter -

- - - - nal bands,

Till the snakes drop, drop, drop, drop, drop,

drop, drop, drop, drop from_____ her head, And the

whip, and the whip_from out her hands.

Mu - sic, mu - sic for_ a_

while Shall all your— cares be - guile,— shall all, all,

all, shall all, shall all,— shall all— your cares be -

guile, all, all, all, all, all, all, all, all, shall all— your cares be - guile.

*poco rit.*

*poco rit.*

# It's Lovely Here
## Здѣсь хорошо
### Op. 21 No. 7

G. Galina (1873 - ?)
*English version by Robert Hess*

Sergei Rachmaninoff
(1873 - 1943)

# The Lord Is Risen
## Христосъ воскресъ!

Op. 26 No. 6

Dmitri Merezhkovsky (1865-1941)

*English version by Geo. Harris Jr.*

Sergei Rachmaninoff

*Per la Signora Chiarina Fino Savio*

# E se un giorno tornasse...

*If One Day He Returns Here*

Vittoria Aganoor-Pompilj *(1855-1910)
(in imitation of Maeterlinck)
English version by Robert Hess*

Ottorino Respighi
(1879-1936)

**Molto lento e triste**

E se un gior-no tor-nas-se che do-vrei dir - gli?
*If one day he re-turns here, what should I tell him?*

Di - gli che lo si at-te-se fi-no a mo-rir - ne.
*You must tell him I wait-ed, wait-ed 'til dy-ing.*

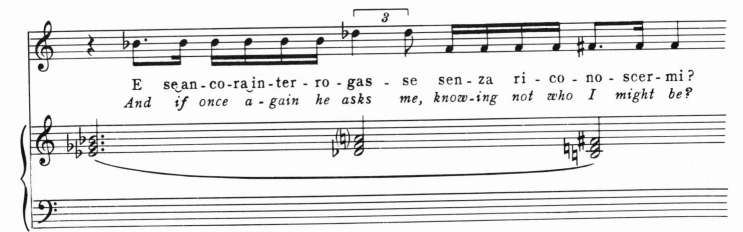

E se an-co-ra in-ter-ro-gas-se sen-za ri-co-no-scer-mi?
*And if once a-gain he asks me, know-ing not who I might be?*

*Par-la a lui co-me fa-reb-be u-na so-rel-la; for-se e-gli sof-fre.*
*Speak to him just as if you would be his sis-ter; may-be he suf-fers.*

*E se chie-de do-ve sie-te, che deb-bo dir-gli?*
*And if he should want to see you, what could I tell him?*

*Da-gli il mio a-nel-lo d'o-ro, sen-za pa-ro-le.*
*Give him my ring of sil-ver, not e-ven speak-ing.*

*E se vor-rà sa-pe-re per-chè la sa-la e vo-ta?*
*And should he want to know why the great hall is now emp-ty?*

Mo-stra-gli che la lam-pa-da è spen-ta e l'u-scio a-per-to.
*Show him then that the lamp has gone out, the door left o - pen.*

Ma se poi mi ri-chie-de dell' ul-ti-ma o-ra?
*But sup-pos-ing he asks me of that fi-nal mo - ment?*

Di - gli che in quell' o - ra... ho sor-ri - so
*Tell him, in that mo - ment... I was smil - ing,*

per non far ch'e - gli pian - ga.
*spar-ing him tears of tor - ment.*

# Già il sole dal Gange

*The Sun O'er the Ganges*

Author unknown
*English version by Robert Hess*

Alessandro Scarlatti
(1660-1725)

Già il so - le_ dal Gan - ge, già il so - le dal
*The sun o'er the Gan - ges, the sun o'er the*

Gan - ge più chia - ro, più chia - ro sfa - vil - la, più chia - ro sfa -
*Gan - ges So bright - ly, so bright - ly is leap - ing, so bright - ly is*

Col rag-gio do - ra-to, col rag-gio do - ra-to in-gem-ma, in-
The sun-light so gold-en, the sun-light so gold-en Is paint-ing, is

gem-ma o-gni ste-lo, in-gem-ma o-gni ste - lo, in-gem-ma, in-gem-ma o-gni
paint-ing each flow-er, is paint-ing each flow - er, is paint-ing, is paint-ing each

ste - lo.
flow - er.

f a tempo

mf rit.

S.M.L.10

# Frühlingstraum

*A Vision of Spring*

Op. 89 No. 11

From *Die Winterreise*

**Wilhelm Müller** (1794-1827)

*English version by*

*A. H. Fox Strangways and Steuart Wilson* ✽

Franz Schubert
(1797-1828)

**Moving along**

träum - te von bun - ten Blu - men, so wie sie wohl blü - hen im Mai; ich
*dreamed of the sun - ny mead-ows Where del - i-cate breez - es play, The*

träum-te von grü - nen Wie-sen, von lu - sti-gem Vo-gel-ge-schrei,_ von__
*voice of the stream in A - pril, The song of the thrush_ in May,___ The__*

✽ From A. H. Fox Strangways & Steuart Wilson: *Schubert's Songs Translated.* By permission of Oxford University Press.

190

fin - ster, es schrie-en die Ra - ben vom Dach.

*morn - ing I shiv-ered and turned and a - woke.*

**Slow**

Doch an den Fen - ster - schei - ben, wer

*But who had paint-ed the gar - den That*

mal - te die Blät - ter da? doch an _ den Fen - ster - schei - ben, wer

*bloomed on the win-dow pane? But who had paint - ed the gar - den That*

mal - te die Blät-ter da?    Ihr lacht wohl ü - ber den Träu-mer, der
*bloomed— on the win-dow pane,*    *And left— me dream-ing and hop-ing That*

*pp*    *dim.*

Blu-men im Win-ter sah,    der Blu-men im Win-ter sah?
*sum-mer had come a - gain,*    *That sum-mer had come a-gain?*

*dim.*

**As before**

Ich
*I*

*pp*

träum - te von Lieb' um Lie - be, von ei - ner schö - nen Maid, von
*dreamed that I loved a maid - en, I dreamed that the maid loved me; And*

Her-zen und von Küs - sen, von Won-ne und Se - lig - keit, __ von __ Won-ne und Se - lig-
*oh! __ to hear the laugh-ter, And oh! __ her smile __ to see, __ And __ oh! __ her smile __ to*

**Fast**

keit. Und als die Häh - ne kräh - ten, da ward mein Her-ze wach, nun
*see. And then with the cock's shrill crow - ing My heart a - woke in pain, And*

sitz' ich hier al - lei - ne und den - ke dem Trau - me nach, nun
*now in my lone - ly cor - ner I dream it all o - ver a - gain,* *And*

sitz' ich hier al - lei - ne und den - ke dem Trau - me nach.
*now in my lone - ly cor - ner I dream it all o - ver a - gain.*

**Slow**

Die Au - gen schliess ich wie - der, noch schlägt das Herz so
*I close my eyes and won - der, If dreams can still come*

warm, die Au - gen schliess ich wie - der, noch schlägt das Herz so

*true, I close my eyes and won - der If dreams can still come*

warm. Wann grünt ihr Blät - ter am Fen-ster? Wann halt ich mein Lieb - chen im

*true, If flow-ers can bloom in the win-dow, And the maid of my dreams be*

*pp*

*dim.*

Arm? Wann halt ich mein Lieb - chen im Arm?

*you, And the maid of my dreams be you.*

*dim.*

# Im Frühling

*In Springtime*

Posthumous

Ernst Schulze (1789-1817)

Franz Schubert

*English version by Robert Hess and Philip L. Miller*

sitz' ich an des Hü - gels Hang, der Him-mel ist__ so__ klar, das

*sit here on the grass - y hill, The sky is bright__ and__ clear,* *The*

195

Lüft-chen spielt im_ grü - nen Tal, wo ich beim er - sten Früh-lings-strahl einst,
*breez - es_ play_ in_ val - leys green, Where I had strolled in ear - ly spring Once,*

*ppp*

ach,_ so_ glück - lich war, so_ glück - lich war; wo
*ah,_ so_ hap - py here, so_ hap - py here.* *I*

*p*

*pp*

ich an ih - rer Sei - te_ ging so trau - lich und so nah, und
*walked a - long be - side_ my love, So close she was to me;* *And*

wie der bun - te Früh - ling schon aus Knosp' und Blü - te_ blickt! Nicht
*buds of spring On ev - 'ry bush, Sweet blos - soms deck the land, Not*

al - le_ Blü - ten sind mir gleich, am lieb - sten pflück ich von dem Zweig, von
*ev -'ry_ flow'r ap-peals, it's true, I choose to pick the branch that knew The*

wel - chem sie ge-pflückt, von wel-chem sie ge-pflückt! Denn
*touch of_ her dear hand, The touch of her dear hand. For*

200

wan-deln nur sich Will' und Wahn, es wech-seln Lust und Streit; vor-
*will and fan - cy change a-lone, And pleas-ure turns to_ strife;* *Love's*

ü - ber flieht der_ Lie - be Glück, und nur die Lie - be bleibt zu-rück, die
*hap-pi-ness_ soon flies a - way, And in its place there comes to stay The*

Es
*The*

säng ein sü - sses Lied von ihr den gan - zen Som-mer lang, den—
*sing of her— and— of my love Through all the sum-mer long,* *Through*

gan - zen— Som - mer— lang, ich säng von ihr
*all the— sum-mer— long,* *And sing of her*

den gan - zen Som - mer— lang.
*through all the sum-mer— long.*

# Die Krähe

*The Raven*
Op. 89 No. 15

From *Die Winterreise*

Wilhelm Müller
*English version by*
*A. H. Fox Strangways and Steuart Wilson* ✱

Franz Schubert

**Etwas langsam** *(somewhat slowly)*

Ei - ne Krä - he war mit mir aus der Stadt ge - zo - gen, ist bis heu - te für und für
*See, a ra - ven day by day Flies a - long be - fore___ me, My com - pan - ion on my way,*

✱ From A. H. Fox Strangways & Steuart Wilson: *Schubert's Songs Translated.* By permission of Oxford University Press.

S.M.L.10

204

S.M.L.10

# Der Leiermann

## *The Hurdy-Gurdy Man*

Op. 89 No. 24b

From *Die Winterreise*

Wilhelm Müller

*English version by*
*A. H. Fox Strangways and Steuart Wilson* *

Franz Schubert

**Somewhat slow**

Drü-ben hin-term Dor - fe steht ein Lei-er-mann,
*Down the vil - lage street a hur - dy - gur - dy man*

und mit star-ren Fin-gern dreht er, was er kann.
*Drones his pa-tient mu-sic, plays as best he can,*

* From A. H. Fox Strangways & Steuart Wilson: *Schubert's Songs Translated.* By permission of Oxford University Press.

Bar-fuss auf dem Ei-se wankt er hin und her,
*Shuff-ling on the ice and slith-'ring in the snow,*

und sein klei-ner Tel-ler
*In his greas-y cap there's*

bleibt ihm im-mer leer,
*not a coin to show,*

und sein klei-ner Tel-ler bleibt ihm im-mer leer.
*In his greas-y cap there's not a coin to show.*

Kei-ner mag ihn hö-ren,
*Not a soul that lis-tens,*

kei-ner sieht ihn an,
*not a heart that feels,*
und die Hun-de knur-ren um den al-ten Mann,
*Look, the ver-y mon-grel's yap-ping at his heels.*

und er lässt es ge-hen al-les wie es will,
*Storm and rain and sun-shine find him night and noon,*

dreht, und sei-ne Lei-er steht ihm nim-mer still,
*Meek-ly grind-ing out the same e-ter-nal tune,*

dreht, und sei - ne Lei - er steht ihm nim - mer still.
*Meek - ly grind - ing out the same e - ter - nal tune.*

Wun - der - li - cher Al - ter,
*Let's go on to - geth - er;*

soll ich mit dir gehn?
*turn and turn a - bout,*

Willst zu mei - nen Lie-dern dei - ne Lei - er drehn?
*I will make the songs and you shall grind them out. __*

# Du bist wie eine Blume

*My Flower*

Op. 25 No. 3

From the song cycle *Myrten*

Heinrich Heine (1799-1856)
*English version by*
*A. H. Fox Strangways and Steuart Wilson* ✱

Robert Schumann
(1810 - 1856)

**Slow**

Du bist _____ wie ei - ne Blu - me, so
*A flower _____ a - lone is like you,* *So*

hold und schön und rein;
*fair and pure and sweet;*

ich schau dich an, und Weh - mut
*And as I gaze I see you*

schleicht mir ins Herz hin - ein.
*Where girl and wom - an meet.*

Mir ist _____ als ob ich die
*I move _____ my hands to*

✱ From A.H. Fox Strangways & Steuart Wilson: *Schumann's Songs Translated.* By permission of Oxford University Press.

S M.L. 10

212

Hän - de    aufs Haupt    dir le - gen sollt,
*bless   you,   And   pray,   I know__ not   how—*

be-tend, dass Gott dich er - hal - te    so rein und schön und
*Ask - ing of Heav - en to keep you    As sweet and pure    as*

hold.
*snow.*

S.M.L.10

# Ich grolle nicht

*What Care I Now*

Op. 48 No.7

From the song cycle *Dichterliebe*

Heinrich Heine (1797-1856)

*English version by*
*A. H. Fox Strangways and Steuart Wilson* ∗

Robert Schumann

∗ From A.H. Fox Strangways & Steuart Wilson: *Schumann's Songs Translated.* By permission of Oxford University Press.

S.M L.10

Schlang', die dir am Her - zen frisst,____ ich sah, mein Lieb, wie sehr du e - lend
*snake that sits and tears thy heart,____ I saw, my love, how love-less now thou*

bist.  Ich grol - le nicht,  ich grol - le  nicht.____
*art.  What care I now,  what care I  now!____*

# Der Nussbaum
## *The Chestnut*
### Op. 25 No. 3

(Original in G Major)

From the song cycle *Myrten*

**Julius Mosen** (1803-1867)
*English version by*
*A. H. Fox Strangways and Steuart Wilson***

Robert Schumann

Es grü - net ein Nuss - baum
*A flow - er-ing chest - nut,*

con **Ped.**

vor dem Haus,
*green and fair,*

duf - tig, luf - tig brei - tet er blätt - rig die Ä - ste
*Lift - ed leaf - y branch - es, and scent - ed the lust - 'rous*

* From A.H. Fox Strangways & Steuart Wilson: *Schumann's Songs Translated.* By permission of Oxford University Press.

aus.
*air.*

Viel
*His*

lieb - li-che Blü - ten ste - hen dran;
*myr - i - ad blos - soms in - ter-lace,*

lin - de Win - de kom - men, sie herz - lich zu um-fah'n.
*Kind - ly the wind ca-ress - es, and laps them in soft em-brace.*

# Der skreg en fugl

*I Heard the Gull*

Vilhelm Krag (1871-1933)
*English version by Auber Forrestier*

Christian Sinding
(1856-1941)

höst - grå dag, flak - sed i brud - te, af -
storm - y night Flap - ping its wings, with a
mæg - ti - ge slag, sei - led på sor - te
cry of de - spair, On - ward it sail - eth
vin - ger bort o - ver hav.
ev - er, cleav - ing the air.
fz
fz
rit.

# Bist du bei mir

*If You Are Near*

Anon.

*English version by Philip L. Miller*

Gottfried Heinrich Stölzel*
(1690-1749)
(often attributed to Joh. Seb. Bach)
*Continuo realization by Kurt Stone*

Bist du bei mir, geh ich mit Freu - den zum Ster - ben
If you are near, Then I go glad - ly To death and

und zu mei - ner Ruh, zum Ster - ben und zu mei - ner Ruh.
to e - ter - nal peace, To death and to e - ter - nal peace.

Bist du bei mir, geh ich mit Freu - den zum Ster - ben
If you are near, Then I go glad - ly To death and

* From Anna Magdalena Bach's *Notenbüchlein* (Music Book), where it appears one fourth higher, in E-flat major.

und zu mei-ner Ruh zum ___ Ster-ben und zu mei-ner Ruh. Ach, wie ver-
*to e - ter - nal peace, To ___ death and to e-ter - nal peace. Ah! then how*

gnügt wär so mein En - de, es drück-ten_ dei-ne lie - ben_ Hän-de mir_
*blest shall be my end - ing, If ev - er_ at my side at - tend-ing Your_*

die ge-treu-en Au-gen zu. Ach,wie ver-gnügt wär so mein En - de,
*love shall grant my soul re-lease. Ah! then how blest shall be my end - ing,*

es drück-ten_ dei-ne lie-ben_ Hän-de mir_ die ge-treu-en Au-gen
*If ev - er_ at my side_ at - tend-ing your_ love shall grant my soul re-*

zu. Bist du_ bei_ mir, geh ich mit Freu - den
*lease. If you_ are_ near, Then I go glad - ly*

zum Ster - ben_ und zu mei-ner_ Ruh, zum_ Ster-ben und zu mei-ner Ruh.
*To death_ and_ to e - ter - nal_ peace, To_ death and to e-ter - nal peace.*

# Befreit

*Released*

Op. 39 No. 4

Richard Dehmel (1863-1920)
*English version by*
*Robert Hess and Philip L. Miller*

Richard Strauss
(1864 - 1949)

und wirst___ mir dei - ne See - - le
Leav - ing___ be-hind your soul ___ to

las - sen, lässt un - sern Kin - dern
bless me, Leav - ing to me our

smorzando

mich___ zu - rück.
chil - - dren dear.

Du
You

schenk-test mir dein gan - zes Le - ben, ich
*gave to me your life's af - fec - tion; Now*

will es ih-nen wie - der - ge - ben;
*back to them I shall re - turn it;*

o Glück!
*O bliss!*

234

S.M.L. 10

# Morgen!

*Tomorrow!*

Op. 27 No. 4

John Henry Mackay (1864-1933)
*English version by*
*Philip L. Miller and Kurt Stone*

Richard Strauss

sehr ruhig (very tranquil)

Und mor-gen wird die Son-ne wie - der
To-mor-row's sun will rise in glo - ry

schei - nen und auf dem We - ge, den ich ge - hen wer - de, wird
shin - ing, And on the path - way where my foot shall wan - der, There

uns, die Glück-li-chen, sie wie - der ei - nen in-mit-ten die - ser
we, the bless - ed ones, shall be u - nit - ed Up-on an earth now

240

S. M. L. 10

* the original poem has "grosses Schweigen" *(great silence)*.

# Song of the Dew
## Росянка
Op. 6 No. 2
(1908)

Sergei Gorodetsky (1884-1967)
*English version by Nicolas Slonimsky**

Igor Stravinsky
(1882-1971)

Larghetto (♩=50)

Зем - ли - ца я - ро - ва - я,
*Our moth-er earth is fer-tile.*

Смуг - ли - ца мать сы - ра - я!
*It gives us food and shel-ter.*

Ни зги в из - бён - ке се - рой.
*My house is poor and emp-ty.*

И - ди, ____ и - ди, ____ по-
*O come, ____ o come, ____ sweet*

*pp sempre*

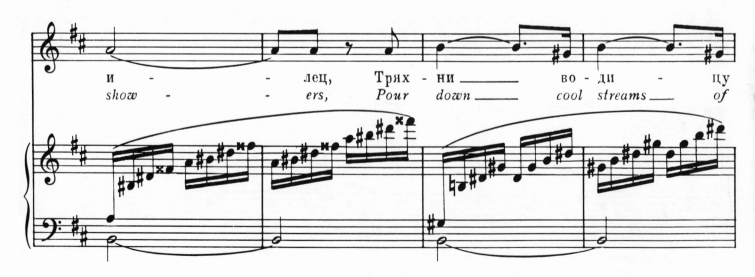

и - лец, Трях - ни ____ во - ди - цу
*show - ers, Pour down ____ cool streams ____ of*

с кры - - лец;
_wa_ - - _ter,_

Сбе - рём ___ во-
_And quench ___ our_

ди - - - цу с ве - рой.
_fields ___ and flow - ers._

Мы за - жда - лись,         Сто - ско - ва - лись,
We have tar - ried          To be mar - ried,

За - пле - та - я__ ко - сы;__         При - то - ми - лись,
Comb-ing our long tress - es__         We are wait - ing,

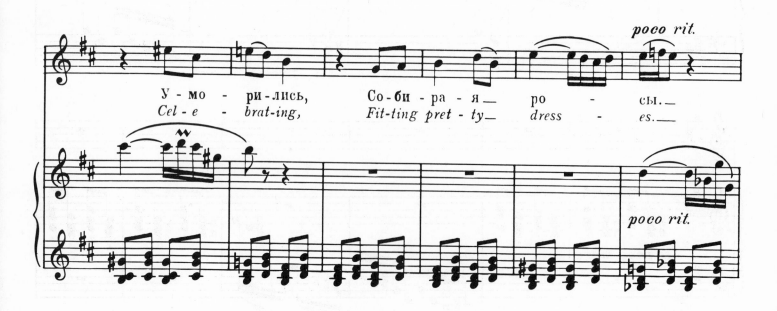

У - мо - ри - лись,         Со - би - ра - я__ ро - сы.__
Cel - e - brat-ing,         Fit-ting pret - ty__ dress - es.__

**Più mosso** (♩=69)

И над каж - до - ю ро - син - кой,
*Sprin - kled with a dew - y show - er,*

При - го - ва - ри - ва - я,
*In the gar - den walk - ing,*

Дру - жку тон - кой, хво - ро - стин - кой,
*We look un - der leaf and flow - er*

При - у - да - ри - ва - я:
*Play - ing games and talk - ing.*

*molto cantabile*
*a piena voce*

За - си - де - лись В дев - ках — дев - ки,
*Oh, fair maid - ens, do — not — tar - ry,*

*mf*

*3*  *3*  *simile*  *poco marc.*

246

S.M.L. 10

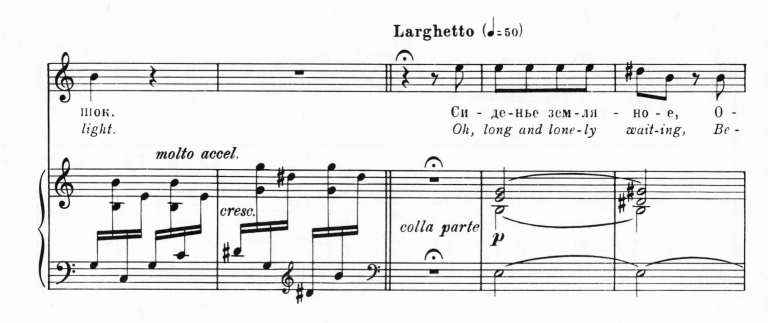

дружки
help us!
В бо - - га ве -
Pret - - ty maid -

руй!
ens!

# At the Ball
## Средь шумного бала

Op 38 No. 3

Aleksey Tolstoy (1817-1875)
*English version by Robert Hess*

Peter Ilyich Tchaikovsky
(1840-1893)

Средь / While

шум-но-го ба-ла, слу-чай-но, в тре-во-ге мир-ской су-е-
there in the ball-room, I saw you By chance through the splen-dor of

ты, те-бя я у-ви-дел, но тай-на тво-и по-кры-
lights, Your fea-tures were shroud-ed in sad-ness, With eyes like the

S.M.L. 10

252

слы - шу ве - сё - лу - ю речь; и груст - но я, груст - но так
*love - li - ness e - qualled by none. When I fell a - sleep at last,*

за - сы - па - ю, и в грё - зах не - ве - до - мых сплю.
*deep - ly dream - ing, My thoughts seem to float far a - bove.*

Лю - блю ли те - бя, я не зна - ю, но ка - жет - ся мне, что лю -
*A feel - ing so strange comes up - on me, This feel - ing can on - ly be*

блю!_____
*love!_____*

# Linden Lea

## A Dorset Song

William Barnes
(1801-1886)

Ralph Vaughan Williams
(1872 - 1958)

whis-tle o-ver-head, And wa-ter's bub-bling in its bed; And there for me, the ap-ple tree Do lean down low in Lin-den - Lea.

When leaves, that late-ly were a-spring-ing, Now do fade with-in the copse, And paint-ed birds do hush their

258

S.M.L.10

# Auch kleine Dinge

*Ev'n Little Things*

From *Italienisches Liederbuch*

Paul Heyse (1830-1914)
*English version (translator unknown)*
*revised by Philip L. Miller*

Hugo Wolf
(1860-1903)

Auch klei-ne Din - ge kön-nen uns ent-zük - ken,
*Ev'n lit-tle things may of-ten give us pleas - ure,*

auch klei - ne Din - ge kön-nen teu - er sein.
*Ev'n lit - tle things we of-ten high - ly prize;*

Be -
*A -*

# Fussreise

## *Walking Tour*

Eduard Mörike (1804-1875)

*English version by Robert Hess*

Hugo Wolf

**Ziemlich bewegt** *(Fairly lively)*

Am
*With*

frisch ge - schnitt - nen Wan - der - stab, wenn ich in der Frü - he
*fresh - cut walk - ing - staff I go In the ear - ly hours*

so durch Wäl - der zie - he, Hü - gel auf und ab:
*Through the hills and flow - ers And the woods be - low.*

_wie's Vög-lein im Lau - be sin-get und sich rührt,_ ___
_as dawn's ear-ly lus - ter Stirs the birds to song,_ ___

_o - der wie die gold-ne Trau-be Won - ne-gei-ster spürt_ _in der_
_Or as grapes in gold - en clus-ter Feel the sun-light strong_ _in the_

dann,
_Then_

er - sten Mor - gen - son - - ne:
*first bright hours of morn - ing,*

so fühlt auch mein al - ter, lie - ber
*So in me, old un - be - liev - er*

A - dam Herbst - und Früh - lings - fie - ber, gott - be - herz - te, nie ver - scherz - te
*Ad - am, burns the spring - time fe - ver, God be - stow - ing All the glow - ing*

liebst und lobst du im - mer doch,
*You still spend e - ter - nal days*

singst und prei-sest im - mer noch, wie an e - wig neu - en Schöp-fungs-
*Sing -ing songs of love and praise, As in ear-ly times of earth's cre -*

ta - gen, dei-nen lie - ben Schöp - fer
*a - tion, To your dear cre - a - tor*

und ___ Er - hal - ter.
and ___ pre - serv - er.

Möcht es die-ser ge-ben, und mein
Would this wish be_ grant-ed: that my

ganzes Leben wär im leichten Wanderschweisse eine solche
warm, enchanted stroll proceed With all cares scorning, Walking in the

*cresc.* *poco* *a* *poco* *f*

Morgenreise!
early morning!

*rit.* *a tempo*

*rit.* *a tempo* *p* *mf*

*f* *dim. poco e poco* *p* *rit.* *pp*

Ped.

# Der Musikant
## *The Minstrel*

Joseph von Eichendorff (1788-1843)
*English version by Robert Hess*

Hugo Wolf

**Sehr mässig** *(Very moderate)*

Wandern lieb ich
*How I love to*

für mein Le - ben, le - be e - ben, wie ich kann, wollt ich mir auch Mü-he ge - ben,
*roam and wan - der, Liv-ing an - y way I can, Go-ing here and go-ing yon - der:*

passt es mir doch gar-nicht an.
*I'm a tru - ly care-free man.*

*[p]*

*mf*

Schö-ne al - te Lie-der weiss ich, in der Käl - te, oh - ne Schuh',
*Love - ly songs of old I'm sing - ing In the chill - y win - ter's light;*

drau-ssen in die Sai - ten reiss ich,weiss nicht, wo ich a-bends ruh!
*Though my strings are gai - ly ring - ing, I've no place to sleep to - night!*

Man-che Schö - ne macht wohl Au - gen,mei-net, ich ge-fiel ihr sehr, wenn ich nur was
*Man - y maid - ens look me o - ver,Hint ing "You're the one for me!" Yet I know I'm*

woll-te tau-gen, so ein ar - mer Lump nicht wär! –
*just a ro - ver: Worthless I shall al-ways be!*

Mag dir Gott ein'n Mann be-sche - ren,
*May the Lord a - bove pro - vide you*

wohl mit Haus und Hof ver-sehn! Wenn wir zwei zu-sam-men wä - ren,
*With a hus-band rich and strong, For if I re-mained be-side you,*

möcht mein Sin-gen mir ver-gehn.
*I would soon for-get my song.*